A Science Museum
illustrated booklet

SEWING MACHINES

by K. R. Gilbert
M.A., D.I.C.

Her Majesty's Stationery
Office London 1970

SBN 11 290090 9

Cover: Singer New Family *Sewing Machine* (*see plate 11*)

Note: All the items illustrated in this booklet are part of the Science Museum collections

Introduction

A sewing machine is not a contrivance for mechanizing hand sewing, but functions by an entirely different principle of stitch formation. In hand sewing the needle carrying the thread passes completely through the fabric and re-enters from the other side. The drawback to mechanizing this procedure is that only a short length of thread can be used and a correspondingly short seam sewn, inasmuch as the whole length must be drawn right through the cloth at each stitch; and this presents a problem because the length of the thread is continually diminishing as the sewing proceeds. Attempts to make a machine, which would imitate hand sewing mechanically, were unsuccessful until comparatively recently and only in 1933 was the problem overcome by the stitching machine made under the Naftali patent, which employs a 'floating' two-pointed needle and devices for handling the free end of the thread. To sew successfully by machine it must be possible to take from a large reel of thread only the small length needed to make one stitch, pass it through the cloth and secure it in some way underneath. The essential element is the eye-pointed needle, which conveys the thread through the cloth, without itself having to pass right through. It has a long deep groove on one side, in which the thread can lie, and a short groove on the other near the eye for the smooth exit of the thread. The point of the needle descends through the cloth, carrying a bight of thread with it, and then begins to rise, with the result that friction between thread and cloth causes a loop of thread to be thrown out from the short-grooved side of the needle. In the lock-stitch machine the underthread, of which there is a supply on a spool, is passed through the loop, which is then tightened in many machines by a take-up lever. The resulting stitch should look the same from either side and the threads should cross over in the centre of the fabrics being united.

The lock-stitch

The machine can thus make a succession of stitches until the supply of thread runs out, with both ends of each thread remaining on their own side of the fabric.

In the single-thread chain-stitch machine the needle descends through the cloth and, as before, rises and throws out a bight of thread, which is however, detained by a looper. The cloth moves on

The single-thread chain-stitch

and the needle in its next descent passes through the previous loop, which is then released. In this way each stitch is retained by its predecessor; and while the seam above the cloth resembles the lock-stitch, below the cloth there is a succession of loops. This stitch has the disadvantage that it may very easily be undone, if it is pulled from the end.

The double-thread chain-stitch machine makes a secure stitch by interlooping the needle thread below the cloth with another thread, which is carried by an oscillating looper and is supplied from a second reel.

The double-thread chain-stitch

Many different sewing-machine stitches have been devised for special purposes and 68 of them were depicted as early as 1882 in Knight's *American Mechanical Dictionary*, but all the machines illustrated in this booklet except one make one or other of the stitches already illustrated. The exception is the cup seamer, which makes a triple chain-stitch.

In hand sewing the needle is inserted at successive points along the cloth as required, but in a sewing machine the needle always operates at the same point in space; and so the cloth must be held against a cloth plate or table by a yielding presser-foot and moved mechanically between each stitch, while the needle is out of the cloth. The most satisfactory mechanism for effecting this is the four-

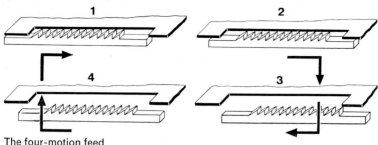

The four-motion feed

motion feed invented in 1854 by Allen B. Wilson. The feed bar with hardened steel teeth rises through a slot in the plate, moves the cloth through a predetermined distance, falls back, and returns to the starting position.

When the feed bar is below the table the cloth can be turned about the needle, so that it is possible to sew in a curve. Otherwise the cloth tends to progress in a straight line with little guidance, insofar as it is not pulled aside by its own weight.

From the very beginning many sewing machines have been designed for industrial rather than for domestic use and over 5,000 industrial machines are now available, many of them of highly specialized application. Thus there are machines for sewing on buttons, making button-holes, sewing glove fingers, sewing the chains of jacquard cards used in pattern weaving—to mention only some of those in the Science Museum Collection. The sewing machines chosen from those on exhibition in the Textile Machinery Gallery for illustration in this booklet include several industrial machines and range from the earliest to the most recent.

Although the sewing machine of today in its various forms is largely of American origin, stemming from the inventions made in the 10 years from 1845 to 1854, the earliest sewing machine was invented in 1790 by Thomas Saint, a London cabinet maker. It is only known from his patent, which remained unnoticed for 84 years, the discovery of which came too late to influence the granting of patents to subsequent inventors. It was a chain-stitch machine, which employed a forked needle preceded by an awl to make the hole. A chain-stitch machine using an eye-pointed needle was made by a German hosiery worker, B. Krems, in 1810, but the first chain-stitch machine to have some degree of success was invented in 1830 by Thimonnier, a French tailor born at Arbresle near Lyons in 1793. Not all inventions have proved so beneficial to mankind as has the sewing machine, but Thimonnier had the misfortune to be probably the last inventor to suffer from machine breaking by hand workers, who feared for the security of their employment. He lived to 1857 to see the beginnings of the sewing machine industry, but did not himself derive any profit from it.

Then between 1832 and 1834 Walter Hunt (1796-1860) of New York invented a lock-stitch machine, in which the second thread was passed through the needle-thread loop by means of a shuttle. The cloth was supported vertically on a movable frame and had to be re-set after a short run of stitching. Hunt did not, however, develop or patent his machine, with the result that the patent of 1846 taken out by Elias Howe (1819-1867), which included the use of a curved needle on a vibrating arm and a shuttle to carry the locking thread, was held to be valid. Howe's machine, which in some respects resembled Hunt's, seems to have been an independent invention, which in the event was the real start of the sewing machine industry.

Howe at first failed to interest American manufacturers in his machine and, sending it to London, sold the British patent rights to William Thomas. Thomas patented the machine in his own name, but subsequently had to issue a disclaimer in respect of the use of the eye-pointed needle and shuttle, when it was pointed out that they had already been used in a machine for applying ornamental stitching to lace, for which John Fisher had obtained a British patent in 1844, although the latter had not at the time intended his machine for ordinary sewing. In 1919 W. F. Thomas, himself a sewing-machine patentee, presented to the Science Museum the machine which had been sold by Howe to his father in 1846.

When Howe returned to New York in 1849 and found that machines by other inventors were being sold, he was able to establish in the courts there his master patent controlling the use of the eye-pointed needle and shuttle to form a lock-stitch. His method of sewing had, however, certain defects: the cloth was supported vertically, the feed was intermittent, and the needle had to be curved.

In 1851 Isaac M. Singer (1811-1875) produced a rather crudely made but simpler shuttle-using lock-stitch machine, which had a horizontal table and yielding presser-foot, and by employing Bachelder's vertically reciprocating needle-bar, could use a straight needle.

In 1852 Allen B. Wilson (1824-1888) found a new and superior way of forming the lock-stitch. The needle thread was seized by a rotary hook and taken round a stationary bobbin containing the lower thread, thus eliminating the noise inseparable from the use of a shuttle. This invention was followed by his four-motion feed, so that by 1854 the Wheeler and Wilson machine incorporated the elements of the modern domestic sewing machine.

The Fisher and Gibbons 1844 patent also included a machine for ornamenting fabrics with a double chain-stitch, which was re-invented in 1849 as a sewing-machine stitch by William O. Grover, who in 1851 and 1852 with William E. Baker, took out patents for their double-chain-stitch sewing machine. The machine was criticised in the 19th century for its larger consumption of thread as compared with the lock-stitch, but it was later realised that this type of machine had the great advantage in industrial use of running for long periods without attention, because both threads can be taken from large packages; whereas with the lock-stitch machine the need for frequent replenishment of the bobbin, imposed by its necessarily small size, is unavoidable.

Although Howe held the master patent, he was unable to put a satisfactory sewing machine on the market, because indispensible patents were in other hands. Eventually in 1856 to avoid litigation, which was embarassing to them all, Howe together with the Singer, Wheeler & Wilson, and Grover & Baker companies agreed to form a patent-pooling combination, which for many years controlled the industry. The Howe patent expired in 1867, but the Combination continued until 1877, when the last patent ran out. Other manufacturers could only make sewing machines under licence on payment of a fee of $15 per machine sold. This entitled them to use the vertically reciprocating straight needle and four-motion feed, which accordingly came into general use after 1856.

The most notable licensee was the Willcox and Gibbs Company, which paid a royalty for the use of these elements in its chain-stitch machine. This machine invented by James Gibbs (1829-1902) in 1856, used a rotating hook to make a twisted single chain-stitch which was more secure than the stitch made by an oscillating hook. It was an inexpensive machine, costing at $50 half as much as comparable machines made by members of the Combination.

A considerable improvement in the performance of the lock-stitch sewing machine was brought about by the introduction of positive take-up in 1872. The loop formed when the needle thread is expanded over the shuttle or bobbin must be removed by taking it up through the cloth in order to complete the stitch. This was effected in the early machines by the rise of the needle bar and by such devices as a spring arm, and also, of course, as a result of the formation of the next stitch. By passing the thread on its way from the tensioning device to the needle through a hole in the end of a lever, which is given the necessary upward movement, the loop is taken up positively. By arranging for most of this movement to take place when the needle is above the cloth, the frictional wear on the thread is usefully diminished.

A few years afterwards the oscillating hook for lock-stitch sewing was brought out as a variation on the rotary hook principle. In 1919 the reversible feed now fitted in the more expensive machines was introduced as a notable feature of the machine manufactured by Vickers Ltd. Although there were early machines intended to be power-driven from line shafting, domestic machines were operated by hand or treadle. A Singer domestic machine of 1889 had an electric motor in place of the hand wheel, but by and large individual electric drive had to wait until electric power in the home became widely available in the present century.

The production of sewing machines rapidly grew into an important industry, which, for instance, in 1871 manufactured more than 700,000 machines. By the end of the century the annual production had increased to 20,000,000. A great variety of machines was available, made by about 200 companies in America alone. Of these 19th century companies only a very few survive today.

Probably no machine has become so widespread and is so generally used as the sewing machine. By reducing the time taken to make a garment by a factor of from 10 to 30 times the sewing machine emancipated women from the great burden of making all the family clothing by hand, and eventually it transferred most of this work to the new factories where ready-made clothing could thenceforth be profitably manufactured. The machine also had a great effect on the manufacture of shoes and other leather goods.

The sewing machine was, after the clock, the first complex mechanism to be used in the home. With no mechanic standing by to carry out repairs it had to be reliable, and as a big investment for the average household it had to be durable. To meet these requirements the moving parts were made of hardened steel and ground to fit, and to make this possible at reasonable cost the Brown and Sharpe Company made the first universal grinding machine in 1876. The firm had, however, manufactured the Willcox and Gibbs machine from 1858 and several machine tools were designed specifically to facilitate the mass production of sewing machines. So the invention of the sewing machine had also a significant influence on the machine tool industry.

So well were the early sewing machines built and in such large numbers that very many of them have survived in good condition for over a hundred years, and are therefore, to the disappointment of their owners, too common to have any value as antiques.

In order to effect an immediate sale to customers without the ready money to pay $100 for a machine, Singer's partner, Edward Clark, devised the Hire Purchase System of selling. The introduction of Hire Purchase not only boosted the trade, but has had economic and social effects, which are more important than those of machine sewing itself, great though these have been.

1   Saint's Sewing Machine

The fact that Thomas Saint, a London cabinet maker, invented the first sewing machine in 1790 was unknown until 1874, when Newton Wilson, a sewing machine manufacturer and patentee, chanced on the drawings included in a patent specification describing methods of making a kind of artificial leather for use in the manufacture of boots and shoes. The general arrangement drawing, which is reproduced below, is accompanied by drawings of details and an explanation of this machine for 'stitching, quilting, or sewing'. It is a chain-stitch machine and embodies such features of later machines as the horizontal table, overhanging arm, reciprocating needle-bar, a feed mechanism, and a continuous supply of thread from a reel on the arm.

The needle-bar carries an awl and a needle, which instead of an eye has a notch at the lower end, the thread being carried by the notch through the hole already made by the awl. The loop so formed below the fabric was caught by a looper and held for the next stitch to be passed through.

At each rotation of the driving shaft a tappet advanced the cog wheel by one tooth, so causing the lead-screw to traverse the table by the length of a stitch.

The model was constructed by Newton Wilson in 1874, but in order to make it work, he was obliged to modify the mechanism below the table. The impracticality of the machine as patented makes it unlikely that Saint actually constructed his sewing machine.

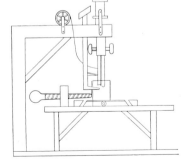

2   Thimonnier's Sewing Machine

The sewing machine invented by Barthelemy Thimonnier, a French tailor, in 1830 was the first to achieve any practical success. The machine in the Science Museum is a copy of an early machine made in accordance with his patent.

His later machines were different in some respects and did not have a fly-wheel. Already in 1830 Thimonnier had 80 machines at work in a Paris workshop making army clothing, but they were destroyed in the following year by a mob of tailors, who feared that the invention would endanger their livelihood.

Thimonnier's sewing machine is a chain-stitch machine which imitates tambour embroidery. The thread is drawn by a barbed needle from a reel below the table, through the cloth to form a chain-stitch on the upper surface of the fabric. The needle passes through a retractable sleeve, which acts as a presser-foot; and with the previous loop round it, passes through the cloth, where it is enveloped by the thread. Leaving the bobbin, the thread passes through a hole in the looper arm, which is rotated at each stroke by a rack and pinion mechanism. The needle on rising, draws the lower thread through the upper loop, thus forming a chain-stitch.

By partly rotating the needle-bar at each stroke, the barb is prevented from catching the upper loop. Its tendency to catch in the cloth is however a disadvantage of the machine, as is also the absence of a feed mechanism. The mechanism in the head of the machine is driven by a connecting rod from the crank-shaft to the fly-wheel, which in turn is driven by a treadle.

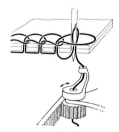

3   Original Howe Sewing Machine

Having built his first machine and a modified version of it for the US Patent Office in 1845, Elias Howe constructed this third machine, which his brother, acting as his agent, brought over to England in 1846 and sold to William Thomas, who patented it here. It is similar to the US patent machine and is followed very closely by the British patent.

In this lock-stitch machine the cloth to be sewn hangs vertically and is fixed on pins embedded in the edge of a thin strip of metal, called a baster plate, which is furnished with a row of holes engaging with a pinion. By this means the cloth is carried along after each stitch; but eventually the plate has to be replaced in its original position and the cloth moved along to allow the seam to be continued.

The needle is curved and near its point has an eye, through which the thread passes from the reel above. The needle is attached to a swinging lever, and when its point has passed some distance through the cloth and is returning, a loop is thrown, through which the shuttle is passed, driven by a picker as in a loom. The needle then withdraws completely, leaving the needle thread and shuttle thread interlocked in the cloth. The needle is curved to conform to the arc traced out by its point, so that it should not displace the cloth when passing through. The motions needed for moving the needle, shuttle, and baster plate are given by cams on a shaft rotated by a hand wheel.

4 Judkins's Sewing Machine

The chief interest attaching to this machine is the high rate of sewing—500 stitches per minute—attained at an early date. This is a copy of the original machine exhibited by Charles Judkins at the Great Exhibition in 1851, where it was the only British sewing machine exhibited. There were also two American and two French sewing machines, including Thimonnier's, shown at the Exhibition. It is a lock-stitch machine, and the shuttle, which is always visible, is held in a carrier working in guides at the front of the machine. The needle-bar is reciprocated horizontally in a straight line. The work is held against the vertical table by a presser-foot in the form of a toothed roller, which is free to revolve. The feeding is performed by a roughened disc behind the work, which receives intermittent motion from the internal mechanism.

This industrial machine was intended to be power-driven by the belt pulley at the rear, but a handle has also been fitted.

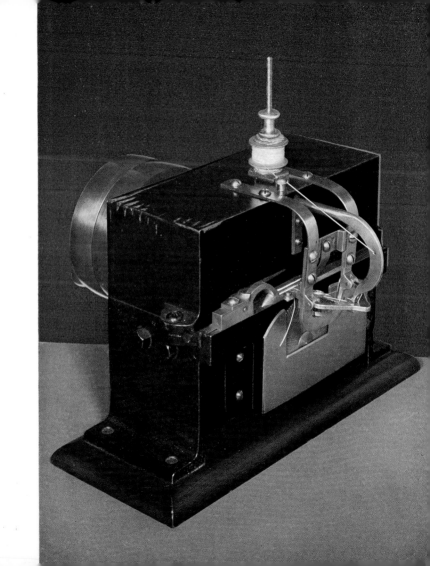

5 First Singer Machine

This is one of the first machines built by Isaac M. Singer more or less in accordance with his patent of 1851. It is a lock-stitch machine, in which the shuttle is propelled by a driver moved by a crank pin on the lower shaft below the work table. The needle motion, obtained from a crank pin on the upper shaft, is straight and vertical. The cloth feed is provided by a finely grooved and serrated wheel, which is moved intermittently by a band worked by a rocking lever from a cam on the underneath shaft, a wooden brake-block preventing by its friction the backward motion of the feed wheel during the return of the band. The feed worked in conjunction with the vertical yielding presser-foot invented by Bachelder.

The machine was packed in a box, which, when opened, served as a stand and contained a treadle connected by a pitman or connecting rod with the handle on the balance wheel. The treadle was pivoted near the centre and was worked by heel-and-toe action. Singer did not realise that he could have patented the treadle, but when this was pointed out to him, it was too late, for it was then already in public use.

The machine is very heavy and more suitable for manufacturing than for domestic use.

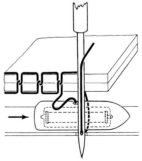

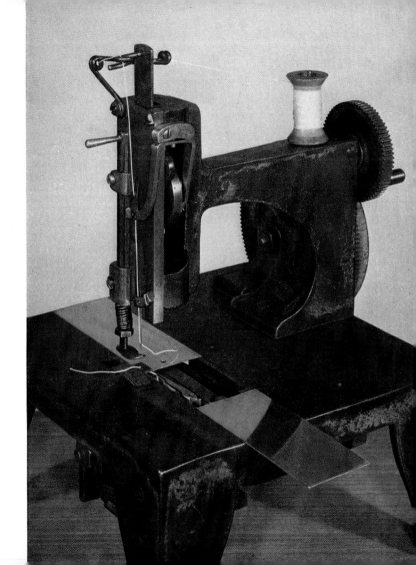

6 Wheeler and Wilson Sewing Machine

This machine is the true ancestor of the modern lock-stitch machine, since it incorporates the rotating hook principle invented by Allen B. Wilson in 1852 and the four-motion feed invented by him in 1854. The machine was treadle driven, but the stand is not shown. The needle is curved to conform to the arc of the vibrating lever, to which it is attached. The presser-foot has an inset glass plate, perforated to allow the needle to pass through, which allows the seamstress to observe the seam at the point of stitching. This feature was introduced in 1861.

The underthread is contained in a thin disc bobbin, which fits loosely in a hooked ring-shaped holder. In the photograph one of these bobbins is shown in front of the machine. The interlocking of the two threads is brought about when the loops of the needle thread are caught and extended by the revolving hook and passed under the bobbin. There is a brush in contact with the hook, which checks the thread until the loop of the succeeding stitch is being extended, which has the effect of drawing up and tightening the previous loop just cast off.

The serrated feed-bar is actuated by two cam forms on the flange of the driving pulley, one to give the vertical movement and the other the horizontal movement. The horizontal return motion is given by a spring and is limited by a cam beneath the table, by which the length of stitch can be adjusted.

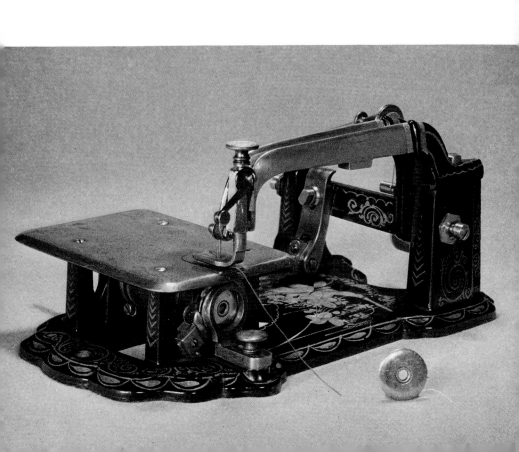

7 Grover and Baker Sewing Machine

The double-thread chain-stitch was invented by William O. Grover, and in 1851 with William E. Baker he took out a patent for a machine that would sew with this stitch. With various improvements the machine was manufactured until 1875 and in all about half a million machines were built. The machine illustrated was made in 1871.

The upper thread passes through the eye of the curved needle at the upper end of the U-shaped rocking lever. The lower arm of the lever is below the table. The lower thread enters the eye at the heel of the looper, which is bent into an almost complete circle in the horizontal plane, and emerges from the eye near its point, the thread lying in the groove in its periphery. The end of the looper is mounted on a vertical twist-spindle, which is made to oscillate through 240° by a driver at the lower end of the rocking lever. The lever is rocked by a cam on the driving shaft, which also works the four-motion feed. As the needle descends, the looper recedes and leaves a loop round the stem of the needle. As the needle ascends, the looper returns and enters the needle-thread loop. The cloth then moves forward and the needle again descends and passes through the open loop of the underthread, which has passed through the preceding loop of the needle thread ; and so on, the two threads being interlooped, but not interlocked.

8 Willcox and Gibbs Sewing Machine

The story of the invention of this popular type of chain-stitch machine is remarkable. In 1855 James Gibbs, a Virginian farmer, saw a woodcut of a Grover and Baker machine (No. 7) in a newspaper advertisement and was curious to know how it could sew. He saw that the needle was attached to a needle arm and could not pass entirely through the material and so could not make a stitch similar to handwork. The mechanism below the table was not visible and it did not occur to Gibbs that there was an underthread. He thereupon conceived the idea of a rotating hook, which would take hold of the needle thread and manipulate it into a chain-stitch, but he did not immediately develop it further.

The following year he saw a Singer lock-stitch machine; but thinking it heavy, complicated, cumbersome, and expensive, he produced a model of a machine made in accordance with his revolving hook principle, which he patented in 1857; and in partnership with Charles Willcox commenced its manufacture. The company still exists, but now makes only industrial sewing machines.

The hook catches the loop of needle thread and holds it while the cloth moves forward. At the next descent of the needle the hook catches the second loop, which in being expanded tightens the previous loop, drawing it off the hook into the cloth. The chain-stitch made in this way has a twist in each loop, which makes it more secure than the common chain-stitch (No. 9). This machine, which was manufactured after 1894, is equipped with the Wilson four-motion feed with stitch-length indicator.

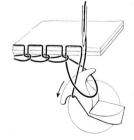

9   Weir Sewing Machine

This small inexpensive chain-stitch sewing machine was manufactured in London by James G. Weir from 1872, the date of his
patent for certain improvements. The looper used to form the stitch
was, however, patented by Frederick W. Parker of Sheffield in 1859.
When the needle begins to rise from its lowest position, the needle
throws out a loop of thread, which the point of the looper enters and
retains. When the needle descends for the next stitch, it passes
through the previous loop, which is then cast off. In this way a chain
of loops is formed below the cloth.

The chain-stitch made by this method differs from that made by the
rotating hook type of machine in that the loops are not twisted and
consequently are less secure. The thread-reel is held between two
cones on the bracket mounted on the needle bar. One of them is
spring-loaded and the other can be screwed in or out of the bracket
to adjust the thread tension.

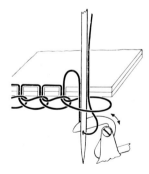

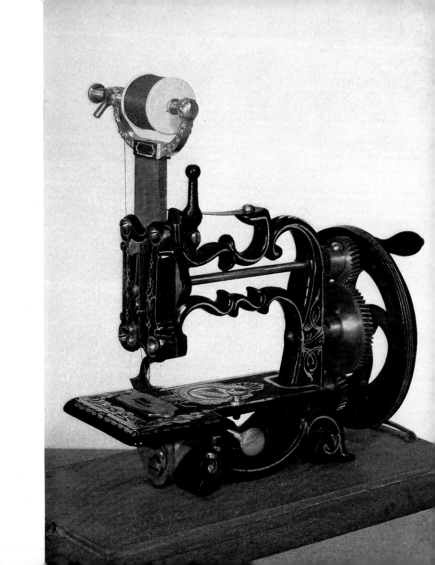

10   Thomas Sewing Machine

William Frederick Thomas patented this lock-stitch machine in 1853. A vertically reciprocating needle is used; and the shuttle reciprocates in a transverse race, from which the end cover has been removed for the photograph. The slotted wooden table fits round the shuttle-race housing and can be removed for sewing narrow tubular work such as a sleeve.

The shuttle-driver and needle-bar receive their motions from cam grooves in the fly-wheel. The feed is given by the presser-foot, which executes a scuffing motion—down and along—derived from two cams on the fly-wheel shaft.

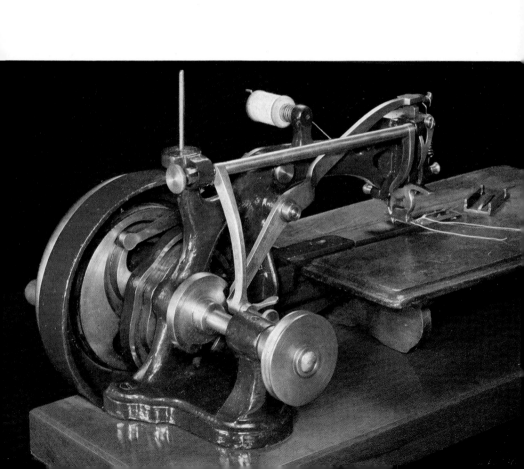

11 Singer New Family Sewing Machine

The original Singer machine (No. 5) was uncomfortably heavy and intended for industrial use, but in 1858 the Company brought out a lightweight *Family* machine and in 1865 the more substantial *New Family* machine. This machine was manufactured for about 20 years, in which time over four million were built. In general appearance it resembles the machines manufactured well into the 20th century. The basic price was £4 4*s*., but it was available 'richly ornamented in pearl, 10*s*. extra,' and in all sorts of cabinets costing up to £20.

It is an oscillating shuttle lock-stitch machine, in which the shuttle moves transversely to the direction of the cloth feed.

The machine is operated by turning a handle acting through step-up gearing, but there is provision for belt drive from a treadle. The main shaft carrying a fly-wheel brings about the motion of the needle-bar and through bevel gearing drives a vertical shaft, which gives motion to the shuttle-driver and the four-motion feed mechanism. The bobbin winder is driven by frictional contact with the rim of the balance wheel.

The tension of the thread is obtained by passing it between the discs clamped together with variable pressure. Between the tension discs and the needle is a take-up lever, which descends to give slack thread for the formation of the loop through which the shuttle will pass, and afterwards rises to draw up the threads to lock together in the centre of the material.

12   Jones Sewing Machine

William Jones of Guide Bridge, Lancashire took out his first sewing machine patent in 1869 and founded a company which still manufactures sewing machines. This hand machine is of a type in production from 1879 to 1909. It employs a shuttle which receives its reciprocating motion from a shaft beneath the table geared to the fly-wheel.

The machine was produced with a view to export to tropical countries and so the unpainted parts were heavily metal-plated to combat rust in humid climates and it was supplied with a steel carrying case.

13   Howe Sewing Machine

This lock-stitch machine was manufactured in 1888 and represents the last form of machine to be made by the Howe Machine Company, which after the death of Elias Howe in 1867 was run by his sons-in-law.

Although from the 1850's Howe licenced the manufacture of sewing machines under his patent of 1846, he did not undertake their manufacture himself until 1865. Meanwhile, from 1854 his brother Amasa had also been producing sewing machines under the name of the Howe Sewing Machine Company, which continued until 1873, when it was acquired by the Howe Machine Company.

Elias Howe's portrait bust appears on the medallion on the front of the machine. This machine has a shuttle working in a curved horizontal race. The treadle stand is not shown.

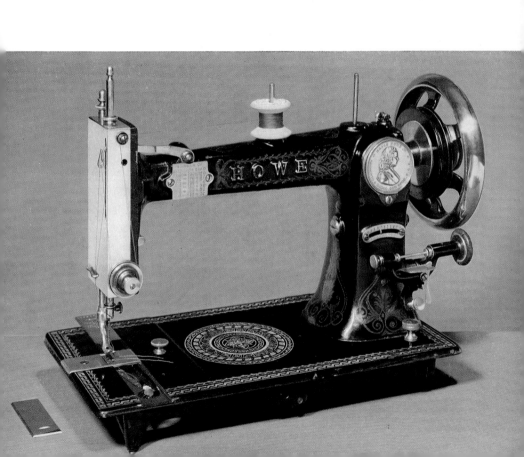

A very small but effective lock-stitch sewing machine was patented by S. A. Rosenthal of Berlin in 1885, and manufactured with some improvements by the Moldacot Pocket Sewing Machine Company of London in 1886-7.

The machine was supplied in a metal case measuring only 8 ins. by $2\frac{3}{4}$ ins. by $1\frac{1}{2}$ ins. and was intended to be clamped to a table. Driven by a winch handle the needle-bar reciprocates vertically and its upward motion is assisted by a spring. The shuttle is carried in a holder, which receives a swinging motion owing to a pin on the lower end of the needle bar engaging with a curved slot in the carrier. The presser foot is rocked by a projection on the needle bar at each extremity of the stroke, so providing a feed motion, which is towards the operator. To have the feed in this direction, opposite to that normally adopted, may be a matter of convenience in a small machine, which uses the table it is clamped to for the support of the cloth.

15   Singer Oscillating-hook Sewing Machine

This lock-stitch machine was manufactured in 1908 on the oscillating hook principle introduced by the Singer Company in 1879. The hook which enters the needle-thread loop, oscillates about a vertical axis through just over half a revolution. The bobbin is supported by a stationary holder and is located off centre; so that the hook is able to carry the needle thread over and under it, in order to bring about the interlocking of the two threads.

The movements are brought about by cranks, levers and cams; with the object of reducing noise by eliminating gearing.

The machine has been partially sectioned for exhibition. The treadle stand is not shown.

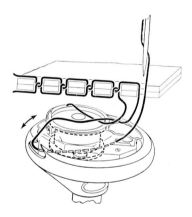

This partially sectioned example of a modern and very versatile domestic machine is made by the Husqvarna Company of Sweden, which originated as a manufacturer of fire-arms in 1689 and started to make sewing machines in 1872.

It is a rotary hook lock-stitch machine and like other modern machines of this type it differs from the original Wilson machine in not having a brush to retain the loop until it is tightened up by the expansion of the next loop over the bobbin. Instead there is positive take-up and the hook makes an idle revolution while the thread is taken-up and the needle descends to form the next loop. The machine is designed with swing-needle facility, so that in addition to the straight stitching it can sew a zig-zag seam of variable width. The machine can also sew in reverse.

Eight different seam-formers can be fitted, one of which can be seen on the left in the photograph. These are barrels with four cams, which control the needle swing and the feed mechanism, so as to produce automatically 32 different seam patterns. The basic patterns may be varied by using different settings for stitch length and width. The machine is also able to sew elastic stitches, which will accommodate to the extension of stretch materials without breaking. It will sew button holes and sew on buttons semi-automatically.

In common with other modern machines it incorporates an electric motor. A low-speed gear with five-fold reduction can be engaged to allow slow stitch-by-stitch sewing when doing embroidery work. The reduction gear also increases the force on the needle enabling leather and other heavy materials to be sewn.

17   Twin-needle Sewing Machine

In this machine, which was built by the Wheeler and Wilson Manufacturing Company in 1890, two needles are mounted on a single
needle-bar and their threads are carried by a rotating hook round a
single bobbin, so that two parallel seams connected by the underthread are simultaneously sewn.

The machine is heavily built and was intended for fancy stitching on
leather. In addition, the needle-bar is carried in a swinging guide,
oscillated in a direction perpendicular to the feed by a rod fixed in
a rocking quadrant on the arm and driven by a cam on the driving
shaft. By this device the threads can be made to follow a zig-zag
course, which is adjustable by altering the rate of feed or the swing
of the needle-bar guide.

The main shaft, leading to the rotating hook, is separated into two
portions, the axis of one portion being placed above that of the
other. A crank pin is attached to each and these pins are connected
by a link. This device which was patented in 1885, alternately
accelerates and retards the hook, so that it is moving rapidly when
it is expanding the needle loops over the bobbin and slowly while
the needle is above the plate and the take-up is operating. This
variable speed motion was designed to improve the appearance of
the stitch. In 1905 the Wheeler and Wilson Manufacturing Company, which until 1870 had been the largest manufacturer of sewing
machines, was taken over by the Singer Manufacturing Company.

As soon as the problems of ordinary sewing had been solved satis-factorily, efforts were made to devise machines for special purposes. To sew a button-hole automatically it is necessary to make the machine sew, according to a built-in programme, a succession of stitches to outline the hole which is then cut in the cloth. This machine was made by the Wheeler and Wilson Manufacturing Company under patents dating from 1884 to 1889 and can sew at the rate of six button-holes a minute.

The work is placed on a movable plate and secured to it by a small rectangularly slotted frame held down by a spring. The needle and rotary hook movements are the same as in an ordinary lock-stitch machine, but the feed motion given to the plate is quite different. The plate, carrying with it the work, receives three separate motions: a quick vibration at right angles to the hole to make the stitches; one along the length of the hole; and a third to move the work across when one side of the hole is completed, so that the other side may be stitched. When the two connected rows of stitches have thus been inserted, a knife moves rapidly down and cuts the enclosed cloth so completing the button-hole.

The special movements of the plate are obtained from a switch-cam mechanism, from which the cover-plate has been removed for the photograph.

19   Cup Seamer

The cup seamer is used in the manufacture of hosiery for joining the edges of knitted fabrics, as in seaming fully-fashioned stockings. It is a three-thread chain-stitch machine employing a needle and two loopers. The illustration shows only the sewing head, which is mounted on a pillar stand. On the base are two treadles: for operating the motor clutch and for opening the feed cups.

The two fabric edges pass first through uncurling guides and then between the two 2 in. diameter cups, which rotate after each stitch to bring the fabric to the chaining finger, over which the stitch is formed.

For the purpose of the photograph the needle has been painted white and three differently coloured threads have been used. The needle with a red thread through its eye penetrates the two selvedges and starts to move back, when the looper with the blue thread enters the needle-thread loop. The looper with the yellow thread then passes between the other looper and its thread. This looper then descends and the needle in moving forward for the next stitch passes between the looper and its thread. These motions result in the formation of the treble over-chain stitch illustrated below.

The machine sews at a rate of 3,000 stitches and 9 ft. of seam per minute. It was manufactured under US patents dated 1936, 1941, and 1948 by the Union Special Machine Company, which is a successor of the Grover and Baker Sewing Machine Company, the originator of the double chain-stitch machine. (No. 7).

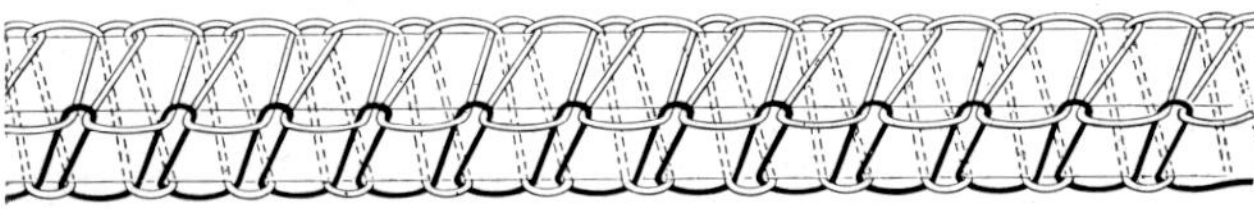

NEEDLE THREAD

RIGHT-HAND LOOPER THREAD

LEFT- HAND LOOPER THREAD

20   Double-thread Chain-stitch Sewing Machine

This Singer 552 machine is an example of a modern high speed industrial sewing machine used for clothing manufacture. It sews at the rate of 7,000 stitches per minute. This means that at an average of 12 stitches to the inch a sewing speed of 10 ft. of seam per second is attainable.

The stitch is the same as that formed by the Grover and Baker machine (No. 7) ; but the looper, which carries the underthread, is different. It is mounted on a universal joint and oscillates backwards and forwards and from side to side, so as to pass on either side of the needle, in order to interloop the threads.

The advantage of using the double chain-stitch in the high-speed industrial machine is that there is no bobbin to be changed as in a lock-stitch machine, and nevertheless the stitch is secure. The thread is taken from large packages, in this case of 10,000 yards, so that the machine can be used for a long time without replenishing the thread.

When in use the machine is mounted on a bench and is driven through a pedal-operated clutch by a $\frac{1}{2}$ h.p. motor, which enables it to reach full speed very rapidly. It is lubricated by pumping oil to the bearings. The presser-foot is also pedal operated, so that both hands are always free for guiding the cloth.

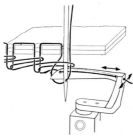

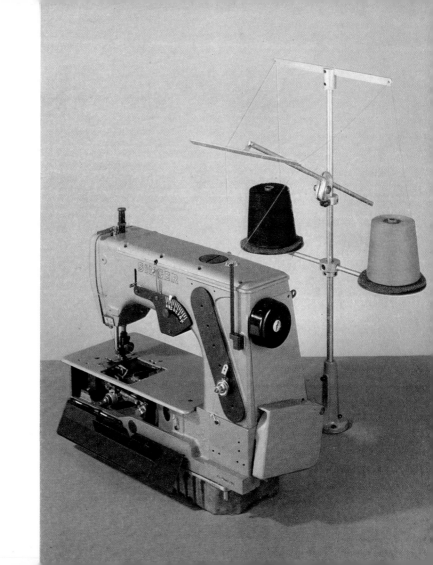

Science Museum illustrated booklets

Published by
Her Majesty's Stationery Office
and obtainable from the
Government Bookshops listed
on cover page iv (post orders
to PO Box 569 London SE1)

Lighting Part 2: Gas, mineral oil, electricity

Lighting Part 3: Other than in the home

Making Fire Wood friction, tinder boxes, matches

Cameras Photographs and Accessories

Agriculture Hand tools to Mechanization

Fire Engines and other fire-fighting appliances

Astronomy Globes, Orreries and other Models

Surveying Instruments and Methods

Physics for Princes The George III Collection

Motor Cars up to 1930

Steamships Merchant Ships to 1880

British Warships 1845-1945

Carriages to the end of the 19th century

7s each (by post 7s 4d)

Printed in England for
Her Majesty's Stationery Office
by W. Heffer & Sons Ltd
Cambridge

Dd. 501679 K120